RAINFOREST ANIMALS DOT -TO- DOT

Susan Baumgart

Illustrated by Richard Salvucci

Sterling Publishing Co., Inc.   New York

To my boys,
John and David

10 9 8 7 6 5 4 3 2 1

Published by Sterling Publishing Company, Inc.
387 Park Avenue South, New York, N.Y. 10016
© 1995 by Susan Baumgart
Distributed in Canada by Sterling Publishing
% Canadian Manda Group, One Atlantic Avenue, Suite 105
Toronto, Ontario, Canada M6K 3E7
Distributed in Great Britain and Europe by Cassell PLC
Wellington House, 125 Strand, London WC2R 0BB, England
Distributed in Australia by Capricorn Link (Australia) Pty Ltd.
P.O. Box 6651, Baulkham Hills, Business Centre, NSW 2153, Australia
Manufactured in the United States of America
All rights reserved

Sterling ISBN 0-8069-0896-3

Contents

**Pig-tailed Macaque
(pronounced muh-KAHK)
An Asian monkey from
the rainforest**

About Rainforests

Rainforests are found mostly in three areas: the Americas, Africa and Southeast Asia.

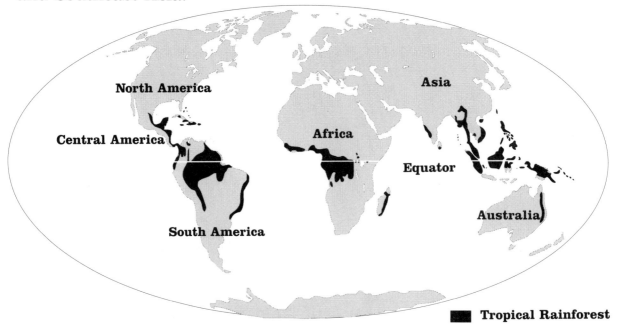

Tropical Rainforest

There are other rainforests. Some are even in cool climates, like the Olympic Peninsula in the northwestern United States. But all the animals in this book come from tropical rainforests near the equator.

What are tropical rainforests like?

They're hot—and humid.

They're wet. It rains most days.

The air is still. Breezes can't get through the thick plant growth.

They're dark. The plants reach for light, grow tall and make a canopy, shutting out the sun.

They're noisy. Birds twitter, sass and caw. Monkeys scream, rustle and chatter. Frogs croak. Insects buzz. Water drips.

They're smelly. Fragrant flowers attract insects, birds and bats. "Fragrant" doesn't always mean pleasant, by our standards. The largest flower in the world (3 feet/1m across) stinks like rotting meat.

They have more insects than anywhere else on earth.

Most animals live in the canopy of leaves overhead. Others live on the forest floor. A few fly by or climb from the canopy to the floor. Only eagles, hawks and a few insects venture above the trees.

The tree leaves are food for the entire forest. Animals eat leaves. Animals eat animals that eat leaves. Plants "eat" rotting leaves.

If someone cuts down a large section of the forest, it can't grow back the way it was because steady, heavy rains quickly wash away the food that the plants need to grow. If there are no plants to hold the soil, the soil washes away, too.

That's why it's so destructive to cut down the rainforests, as large companies have been doing. It destroys the forest, and any possibility of growing food. Animals that need large areas for finding food die off when left with only scattered patches. And the animals that depend on them for food also die off.

We are all affected—even if we live in colder, drier places. We eat foods from the rainforest—cocoa, coffee and pineapples. We take medicines from the rainforest. And we breathe the oxygen that the rainforest trees create for the entire planet.

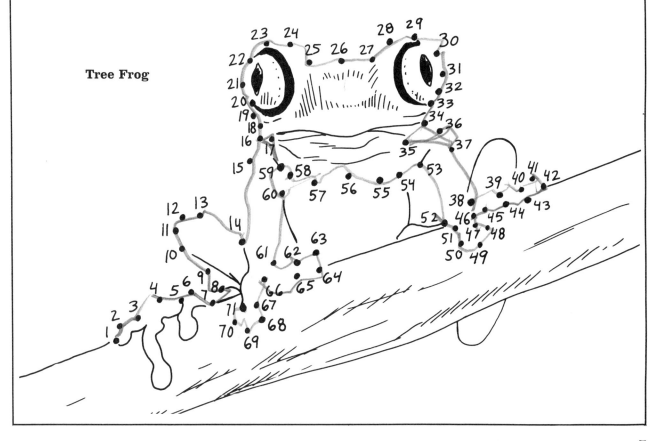

Tree Frog

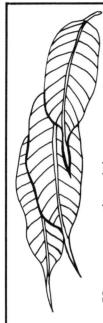

Anaconda

Pronounced: AN-uh-KAHN-da

Where it lives: South America
                          In and along rivers and
                          climbing low branches

Size: Adults often grow to about
                          25 feet (7.6m) long, and
                          some have been reported
                          over 37 feet (11.5m) long.
                          Two-hundred-pounders
                          (90kg) are common.

What it eats: Rodents, pigs, birds and
                          other animals

The anaconda is the largest living snake in the
world. The one in the picture is wrapped around a
7-foot (2.1m) crocodilian called a caiman. Despite its
large teeth and scaly armor, the caiman will be
squeezed till it cannot fill its lungs with air—and so
will die. Then the anaconda will swallow it whole.

Color: Black and shades of brown

The anaconda
likes to eat
_ _ _ _ _. This
one is called a
peccary.

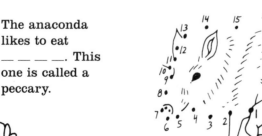

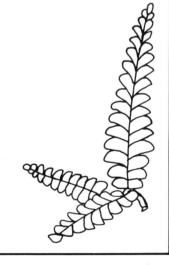

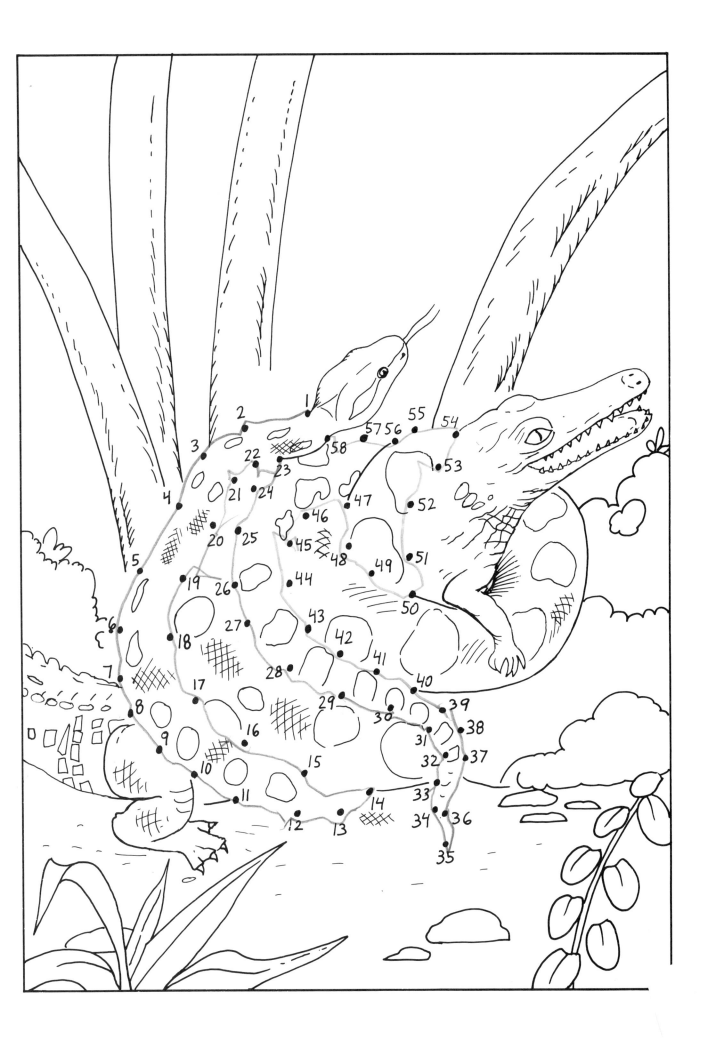

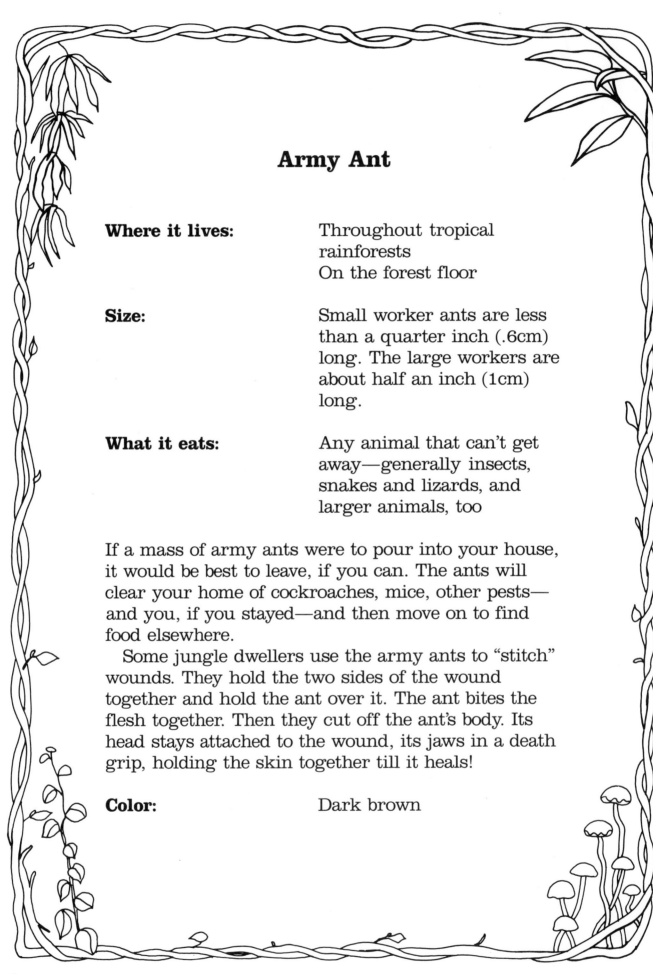

Army Ant

Where it lives: Throughout tropical
rainforests
On the forest floor

Size: Small worker ants are less
than a quarter inch (.6cm)
long. The large workers are
about half an inch (1cm)
long.

What it eats: Any animal that can't get
away—generally insects,
snakes and lizards, and
larger animals, too

If a mass of army ants were to pour into your house,
it would be best to leave, if you can. The ants will
clear your home of cockroaches, mice, other pests—
and you, if you stayed—and then move on to find
food elsewhere.

Some jungle dwellers use the army ants to "stitch"
wounds. They hold the two sides of the wound
together and hold the ant over it. The ant bites the
flesh together. Then they cut off the ant's body. Its
head stays attached to the wound, its jaws in a death
grip, holding the skin together till it heals!

Color: Dark brown

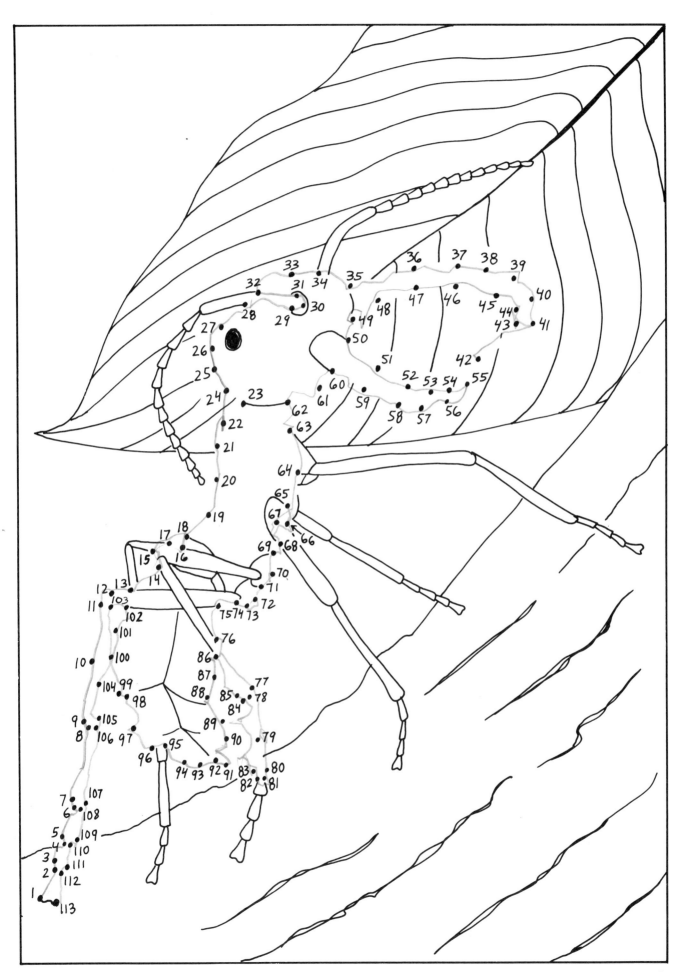

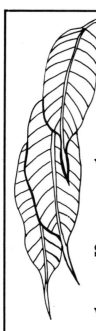

Arrow Poison Frog

Where it lives: Central and South America
From the ground to high in
the trees

Size: Under an inch (2.5cm) long,
with slender legs

What it eats: Mostly insects

Arrow poison frogs can hurt you or even kill you if
you touch them. Touching releases poisons in their
skin. Native people have learned how to heat the
frogs to "sweat out" the poison, which they then
smear on the tips of blowgun darts or arrowheads.
One frog provides enough poison to treat 30 to 50
weapons!

Color: Bright colors—reds,
yellows, blues, greens and
black

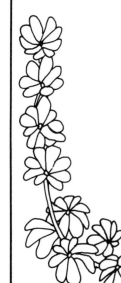

Just about any

_ _ _ _ _ _ _

flying by makes a
good meal for
frogs.

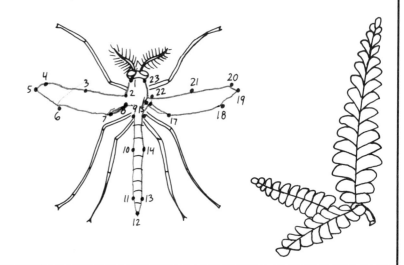

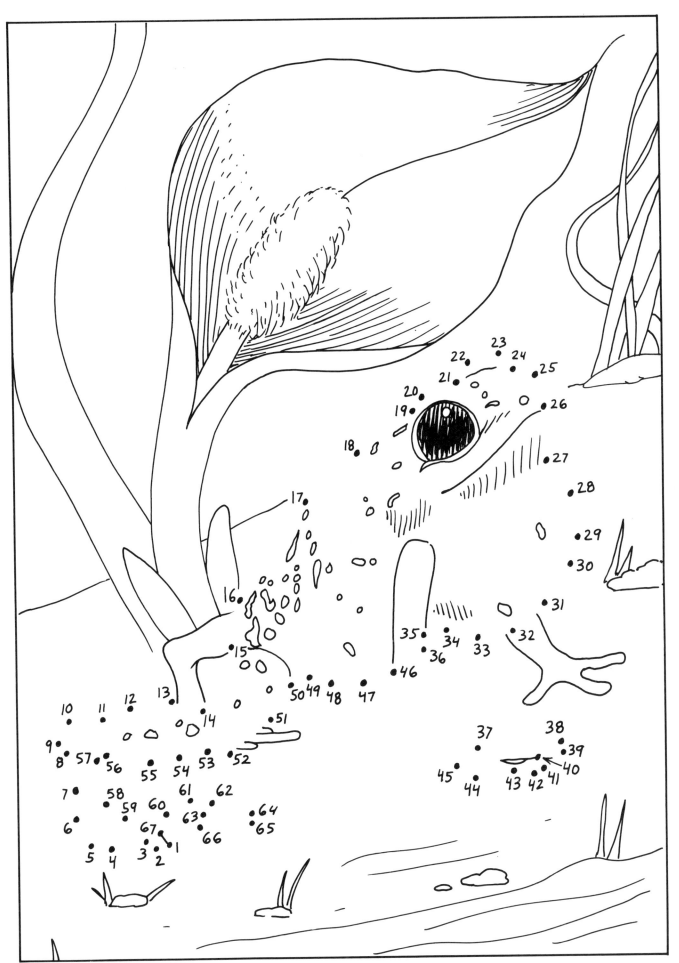

Birdwing Butterfly

Where it lives: Southeast Asia
Mostly high in the trees, though some fly down to the ground once in the morning to drink or feed.

Size: The largest has a wingspan of over 10 inches (25cm).

What it eats: Like other butterflies, the birdwing does most of its eating as a caterpillar. What was a mouth for munching plants as a caterpillar becomes a long straw-like tube for sucking nectar as a butterfly.

The birdwing butterfly is among the largest butterflies in the world. It is called "birdwing" because it looks more like a bird than a butterfly when it flies overhead.

Color: Most of the wing is black. The markings are green or greenish yellow.

Birdwings put their strawlike tongue down the center of these _ _ _ _ _ _ _ to sip nectar.

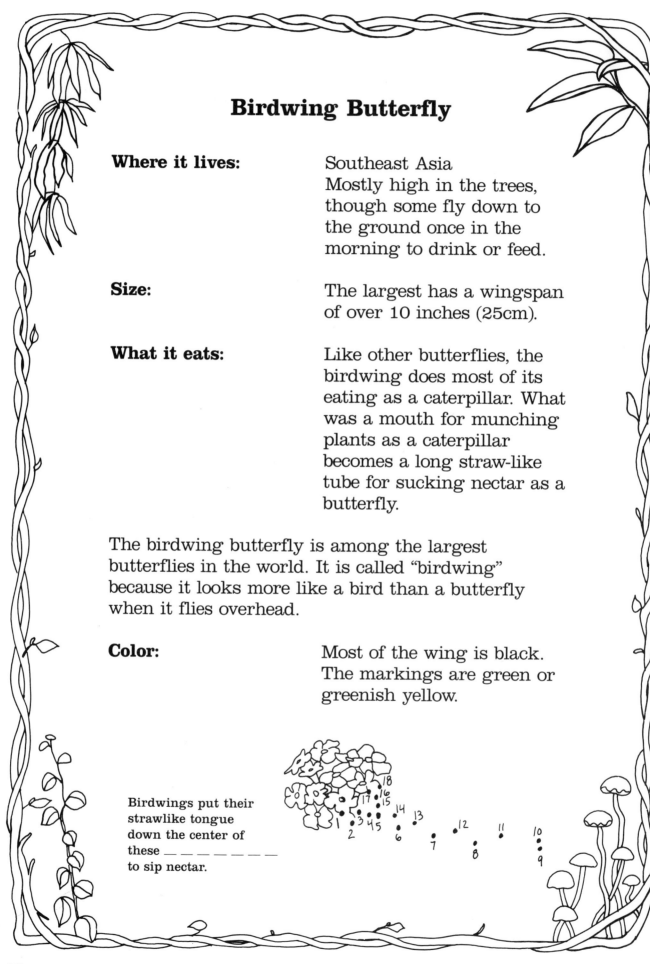

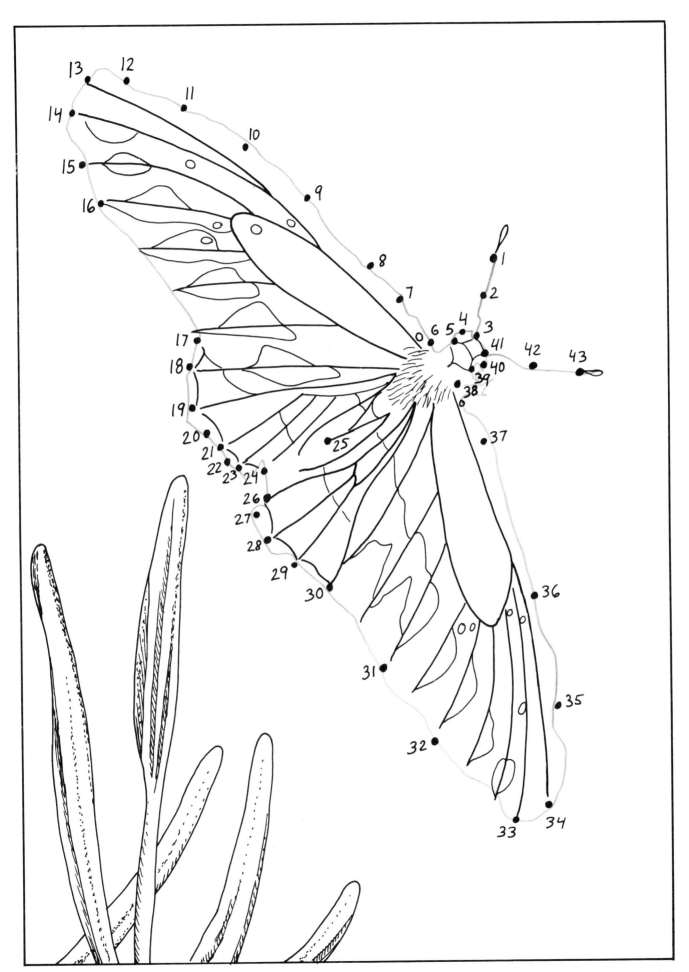

13

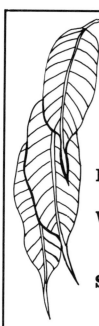

Chameleon

Pronounced:	ka-MEE-lee-un
Where it lives:	Africa In the trees
Size:	From several inches to nearly a foot (1m) long
What it eats:	Insects

The chameleon grabs dinner with a long sticky tongue that may be longer than its body! The tongue shoots out and back in a flash (⁴⁄₁₀₀ths of a second)! With this speed and its excellent aim, the chameleon hardly ever misses.

A chameleon may change color to match its surroundings. It can get darker or lighter to warm or cool itself (lighter colors reflect sunlight and therefore are cooler).

Color:	Chameleons are usually brown and tan or green and yellowish green.

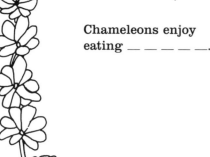

Chameleons enjoy eating _ _ _ _ _ _ .

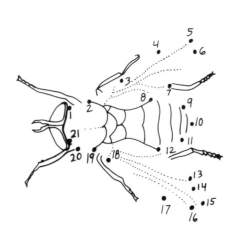

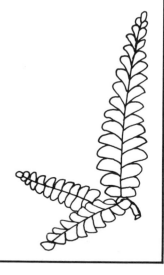

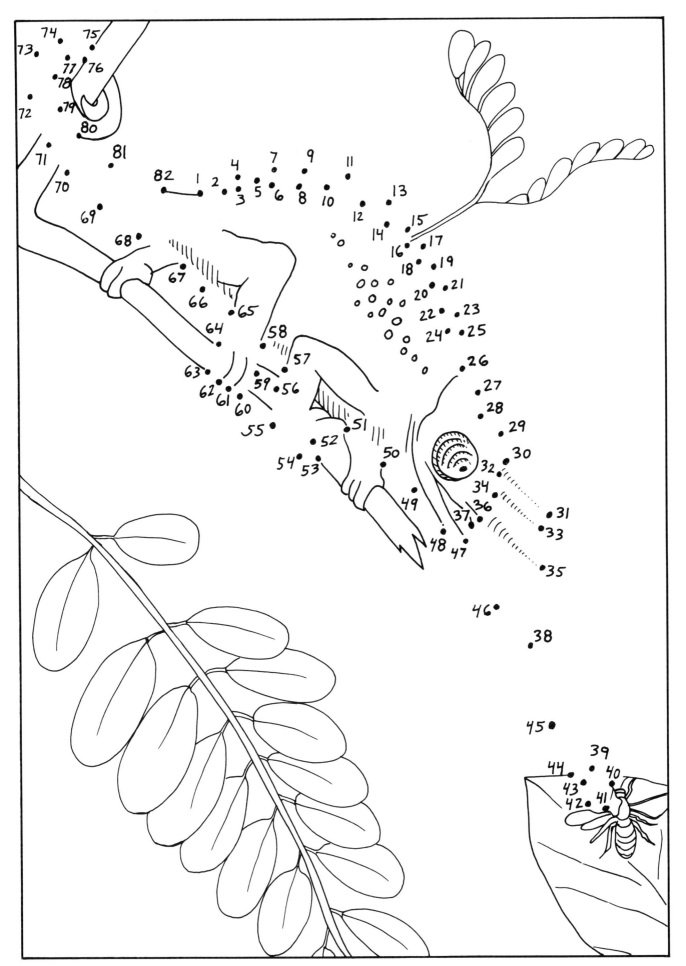

15

Chimpanzee

Pronounced: chim-pan-ZEE

Where it lives: Africa
In the trees and on the ground

Size: The chimpanzee often reaches five feet (1.5m) tall and 110 pounds (50kg), the size of a small woman.

What it eats: Plants and meat. Sometimes chimps work together to trap an animal and then call the rest of the clan for dinner.

Chimps live in groups of up to 100 animals. Males often quarrel with each other, but females are usually good friends.

Color: Tan skin, tan whiskers, black hair and light orange-brown eyes. Unlike human eyes, the "whites" of the chimp's eyes are brown!

Chimpanzees aren't the only ones who like to eat

– – – – – – – – –

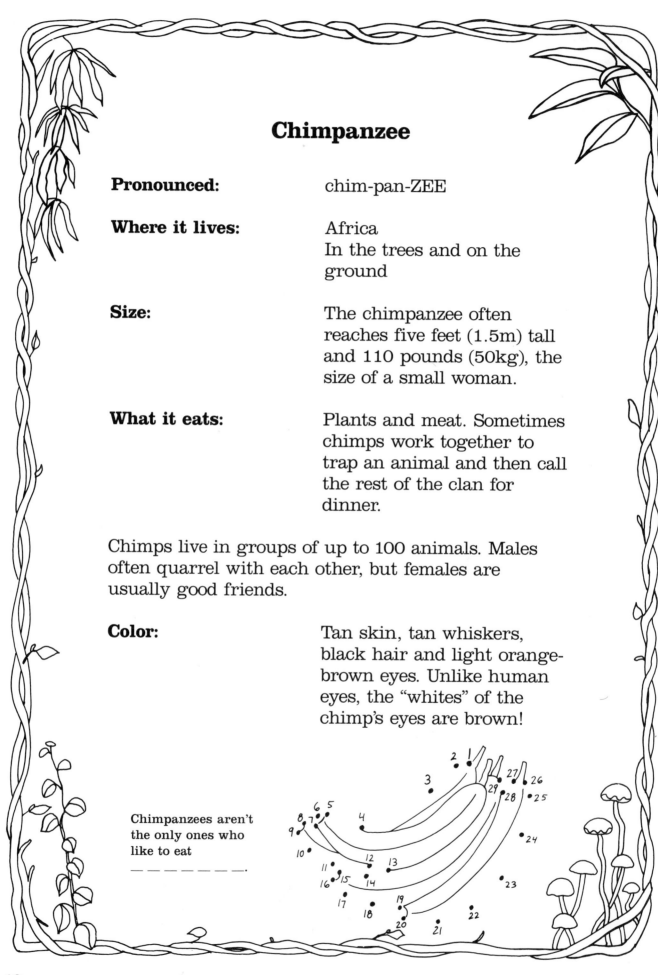

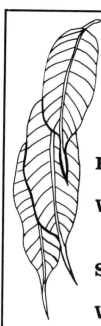

Fer de Lance

Pronounced:	FUR-duh-lans
Where it lives:	Central and South America, and in the West Indies
Size:	Up to seven feet (2m) long
What it eats:	Rats, opossums and any other mammals that come within striking range

Waiting quietly by the side of the trail, this snake strikes whatever happens to pass by. It presses its fangs in deeply, squirts the poison through them, and then backs off to wait for the death of its victim. If the prey manages to stumble away, the snake will follow its scent and body heat. Those little pits on the nose of the snake are very sensitive to heat.

The fer de lance is considered the most dangerous snake in Central America. More than half the snakebites that take place each year—and most of the deaths—are from the fer de lance.

Color:	Patterns of brown, grey and tan that help the snake hide among leaves and twigs

A fer de lance can easily snag an

– – – – – – – – .

19

Flying Squirrel

Where it lives: Southeast Asia
In the treetops

Size: The flying squirrel can
grow to three feet long (1m)
when it stretches out.

What it eats: Fruit, nuts and leaf buds

Although called "flying," this squirrel doesn't flap its
wings like a bird. It doesn't have wings. It glides,
like a hang glider or sky diver.

After circling a tree trunk for a few minutes, it
will suddenly leap off into space, sailing 100 to 125
feet (30 to 37m). The skin that is like a webbing
between its legs forms a kind of "parachute."
Towards the end of its flight, it swoops up, grabs
onto a tree with its clawed feet and scampers up the
trunk, the folds of its webbed skin flapping like an
oversized overcoat.

Color: Creamy underneath,
greyish above, with a pink
nose and feet

Many animals,
including the

— — — — — —

— — — — — — — —,
enjoy eating mangoes, a
red-yellow fruit.

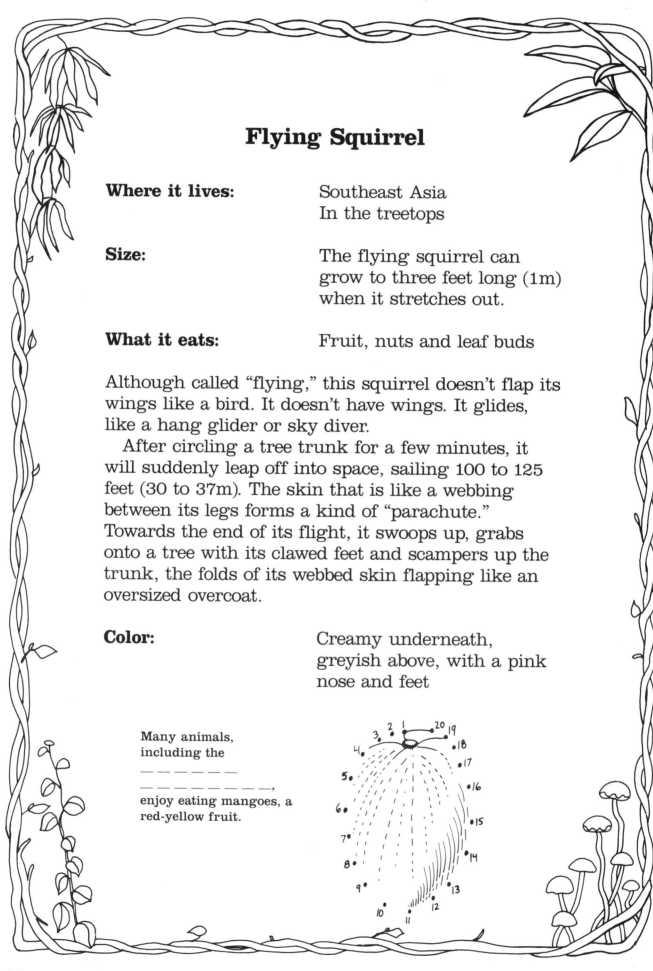

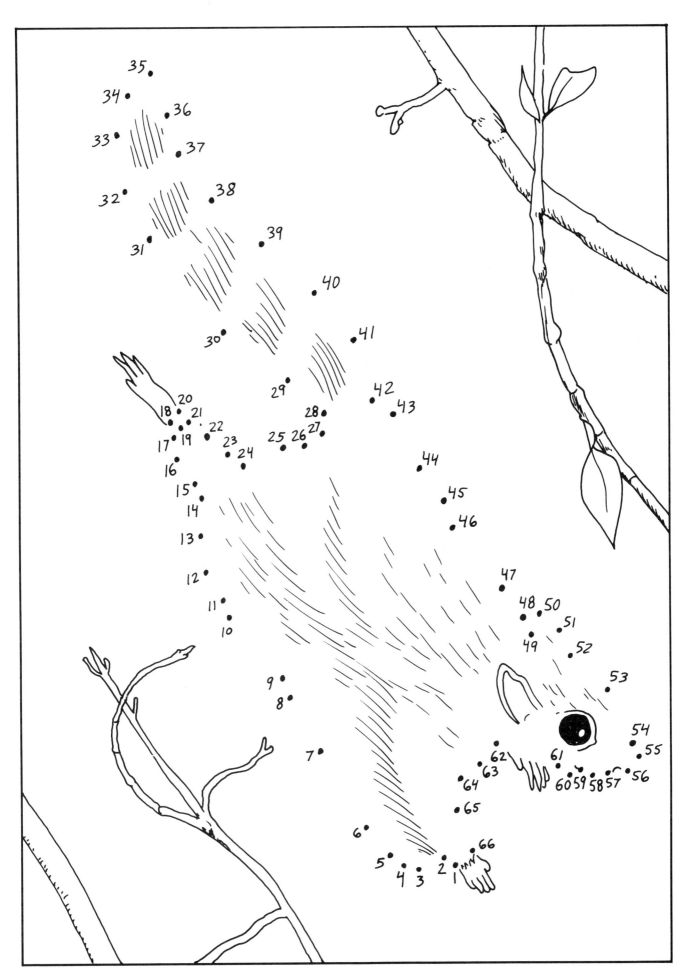

21

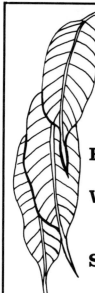

Gibbon

Pronounced: GIB-un

Where it lives: Southeast Asia
                          Mostly in the trees

Size: About three feet (1m) tall
                          and 15 pounds (7kg). Its
                          arms are so long that its
                          "hands" would drag on the
                          ground if it didn't hold
                          them up.

What it eats: Mostly leaves and fruit,
                          although it sometimes eats
                          insects, spiders, birds' eggs
                          and other small animals

The gibbon swings through the trees extremely fast,
using one arm and then the other. It sometimes lets
go and "flies" through the air to branches as far as
20 feet (6m) away. Some people say they have seen
the gibbon change direction in midair. The gibbon is
friendly to humans.

Color: Brown, with a creamy circle
                          around a black face

Mangosteen is a
tropical fruit enjoyed
by — — — — — — —.

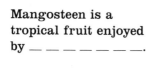

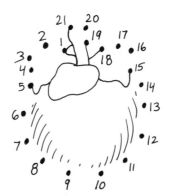

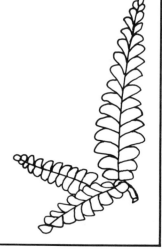

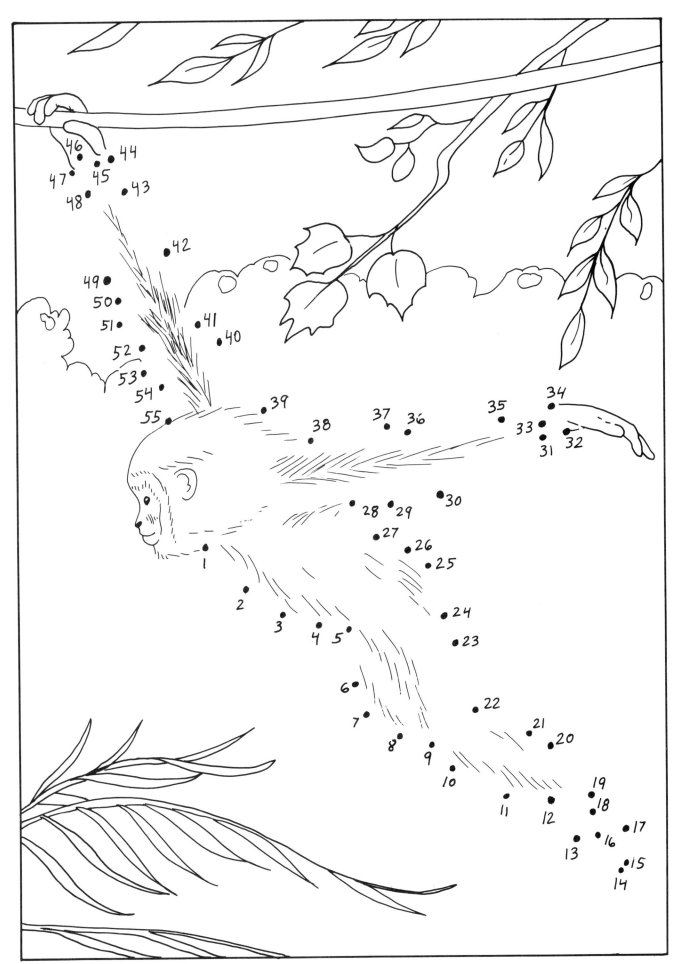

Gorilla

Where it lives: Africa
On the ground, though females and children may climb carefully into low tree branches

Size: The largest apes in the jungle, males may be nearly six feet (1.8m) tall and weigh 450 pounds (204kg).

What it eats: Mostly leaves

Did you see the movie *King Kong* about the gorilla who climbs to the top of the Empire State Building? Well, gorillas cannot walk upright and males don't climb at all. In nature, they are gentle giants—not at all monster material!

Color: Black with brown eyes. Older males have a patch of silvery hair on their backs.

Besides

— — — — — —, gorillas eat the inside of the stem of wild celery.

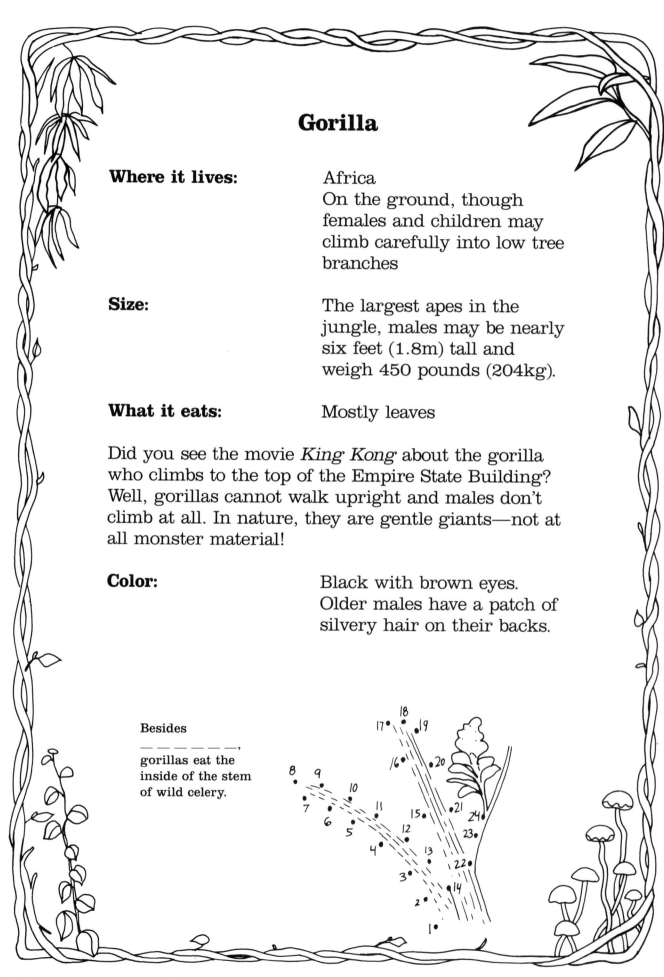

Harpy Eagle

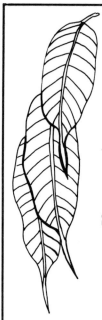

Where it lives:　　　South America
In the tallest trees

Size:　　　About three feet (1m) long
from head to tail. Its feet are
larger than a man's hand. It
is the largest eagle in the
world.

What it eats:　　　Monkeys, sloths, opossums,
tree porcupines, macaws,
snakes and others

Rainforest eagles do not spend time soaring slowly
above the trees, as eagles do in drier climates.
Instead, they make short flights from branch to
branch. When chasing prey, harpy eagles sometimes
dive at 50 miles (80km) per hour.

Color:　　　Shades of grey, from nearly
black to medium, and off-
white

Tropical
eagles love to
eat _ _ _ _ _ _ _
meat.

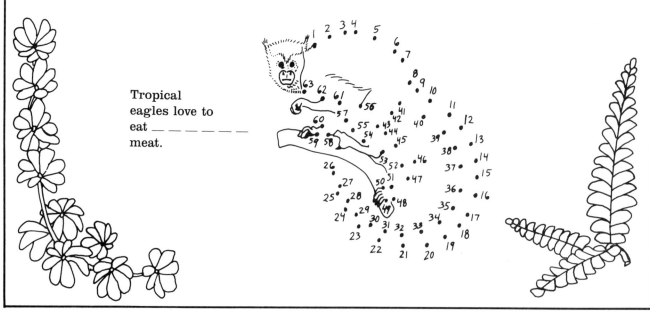

Hercules Beetle

Pronounced: HER-kew-leez BEE-tul

Where it lives: Central and South America
On the ground, tucked in
nooks and crannies

Size: Over five inches (12.7cm)
long, most of which is the
length of the head and
horns

What it eats: Rotting wood

Almost one third of all known types of animals in
the world are beetles! Some kinds, including the
Hercules, are among the few creatures besides
termites that eat rotting wood. They are part of the
great army of recyclers in the rainforest.

Color: Black head and legs, a
green "cloak" on its back
and a brown body

Mmm, delicious—
the _ _ _ _ _ _ _
stump of a tree!

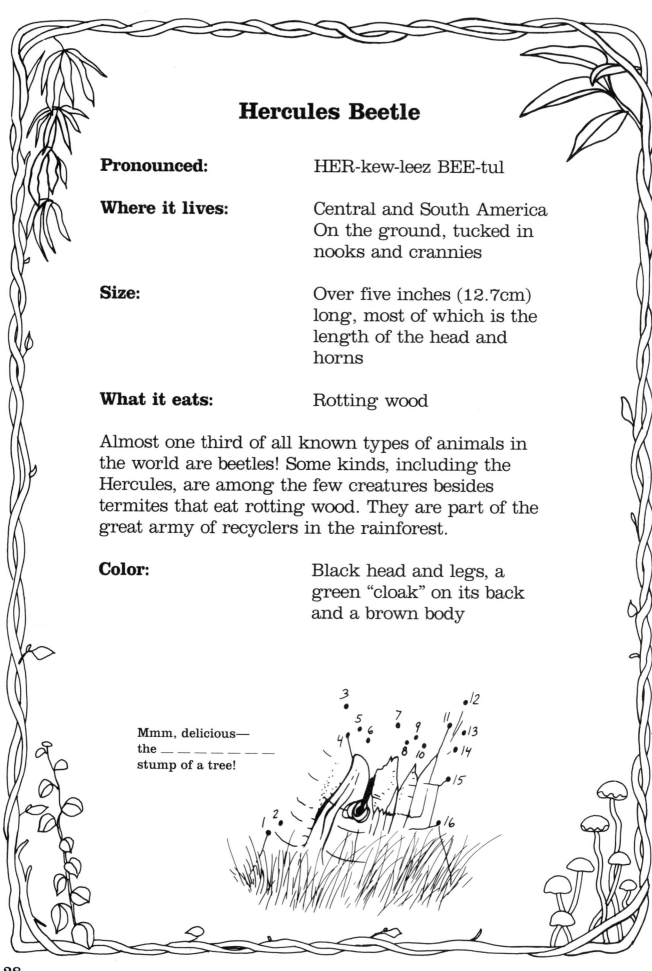

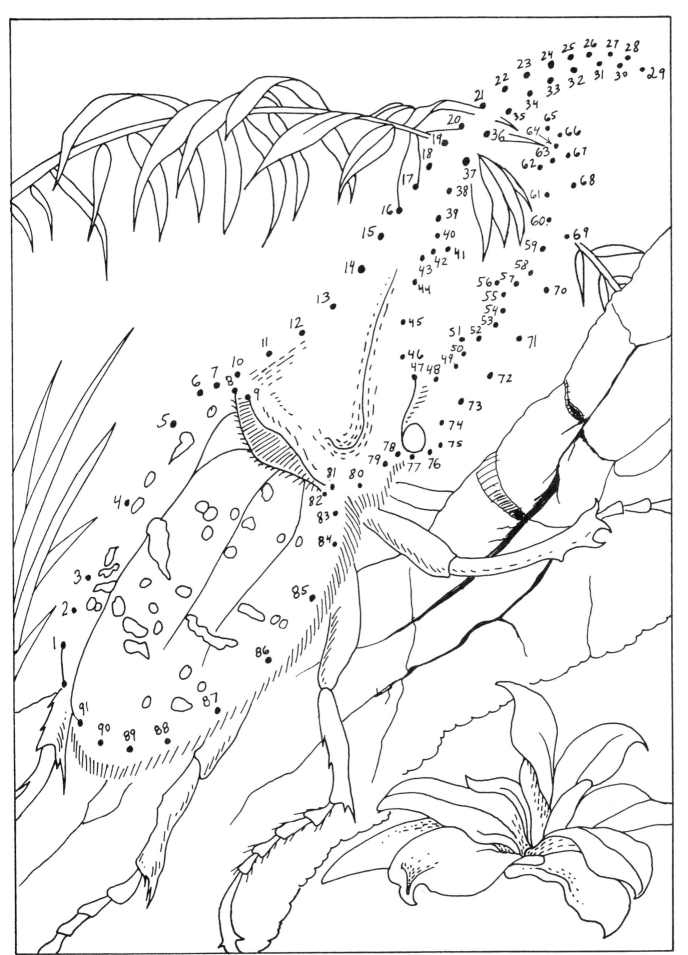

Howler Monkey

Where it lives:	Central and South America Almost always in the trees
Size:	Largest of the American monkeys, the male is about the size of a large dog.
What it eats:	Mostly leaves. Its favorite food is wild figs.

Besides screaming to settle territorial claims, these monkeys howl in the morning when they wake up and in the evening before settling down. In spite of the noise they make, they are pretty calm compared to most monkeys. They move slowly and snooze much of their lives away, draping their four legs over a branch like a soggy fur blanket.

Color:	Black or brownish red

Here's one of the howler's favorites—a
— — —.

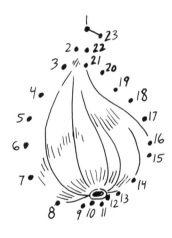

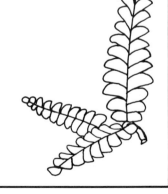

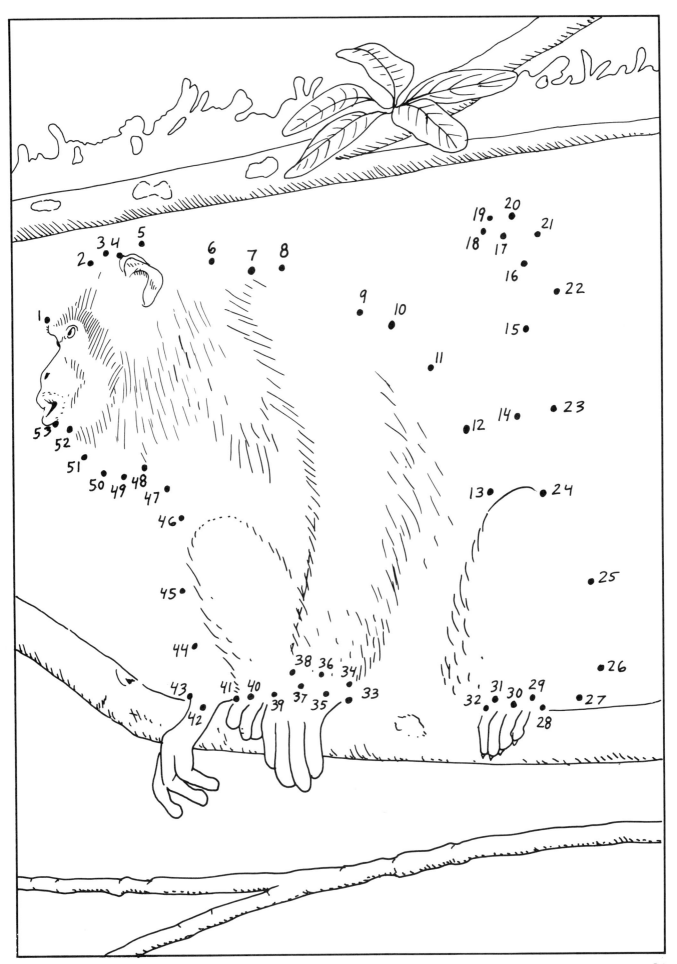

Hummingbird

Where it lives: North and South America
                        Among flowers

Size: Only a few inches long. The
                        smallest, the "bee"
                        hummingbird, is hardly
                        larger than a bumblebee—
                        the smallest bird in the
                        world.

What it eats: Nectar, the sweet liquid at
                        the base of some flowers

The hummingbird can fly forward, backwards and
hover in the air. Its wings beat as many as 100 times
per second. While you say "one-one-thousand," those
wings have flapped 100 times! When flying forward,
it can move 40 miles (64km) per hour.

Color: There are over 300 kinds of
                        hummingbird. All have
                        feathers in extremely
                        vibrant and varied colors.

This flower has
_ _ _ _ _ _ _ some
hummingbirds
drink.

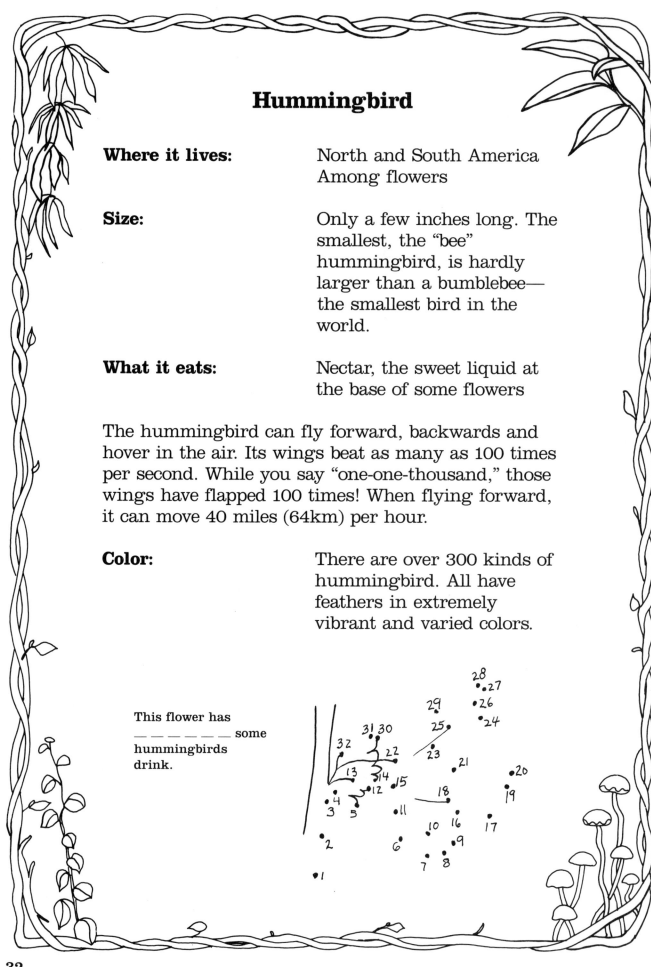

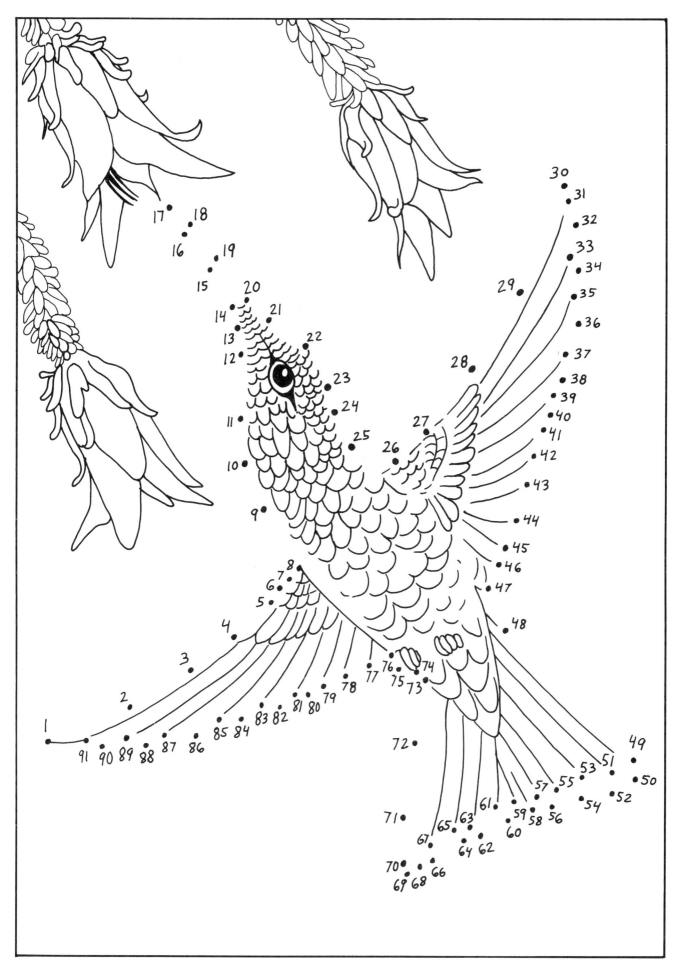

Jaguar

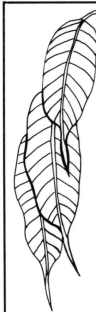

Pronounced: JAG-wahr

Where it lives: The Americas
It hides and hunts in the bushes and from lower tree branches.

Size: Taller than most basketball players when standing on its hind legs, the jaguar may grow to seven and a half feet (2.3m) long and weigh 250 pounds (113kg). A paw print can be as big as a person's face.

What it eats: Just about every animal that has a backbone: deer, squirrels, opossums, monkeys, birds and other animals. It even fishes in the river with its paws.

The jaguar has massively strong jaws. Cracking a human skull is about as challenging as splitting a ripe cantaloupe.

Color: The underside has a creamy background color; the sides and flanks are an orange brown. The spots and rings are black. The rings are filled with orange and have a black spot in the middle.

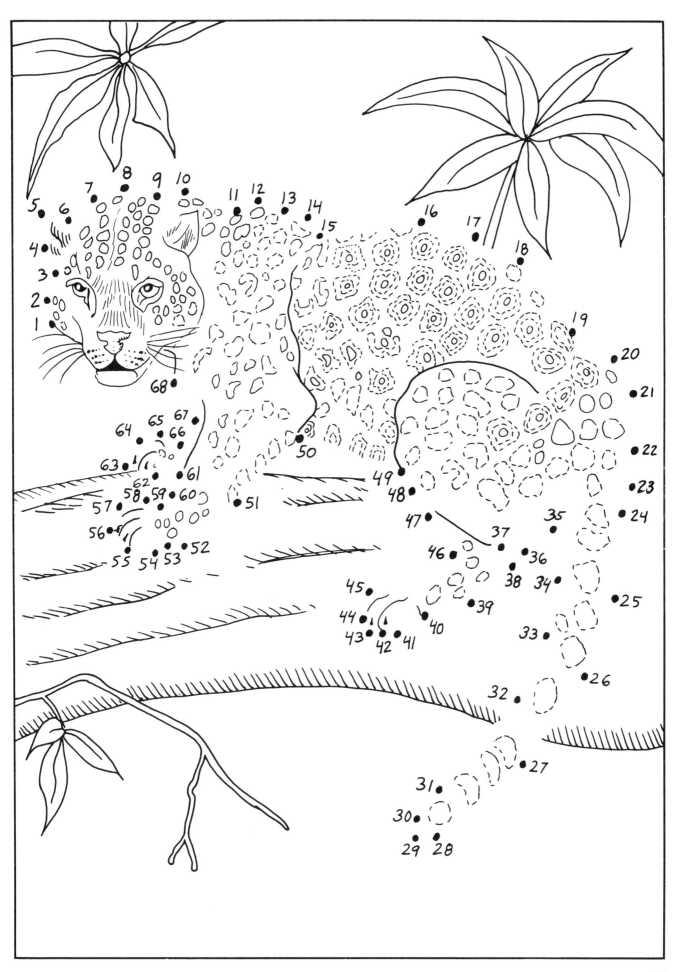

Jungle Fowl

Where it lives: Southeast Asia
                      Mostly on the ground

Size: Like a chicken

What it eats: Seeds, fruit, buds and
                      insects, particularly
                      termites

The male jungle fowl is quick to fight. He attacks
rivals with sharp spurs that poke out of the back of
each leg. Very showy, he courts females with elegant
bowing and dancing. He even strums a love song,
creating a harplike sound on his flight feathers with
his foot. And, yes, in the early morning, he crows.

Chickens, whose meat and eggs we eat, were bred
from jungle fowl over 1,000 years ago.

Color: The female is a dull brown.
                      The male is brightly
                      colored. Although some of
                      his body is black with a
                      green shine, he has orange-
                      bronze, red, glossy green
                      and a few white feathers.

Jungle fowl find

_ _ _ _ _ _ _ _ _

delicious.

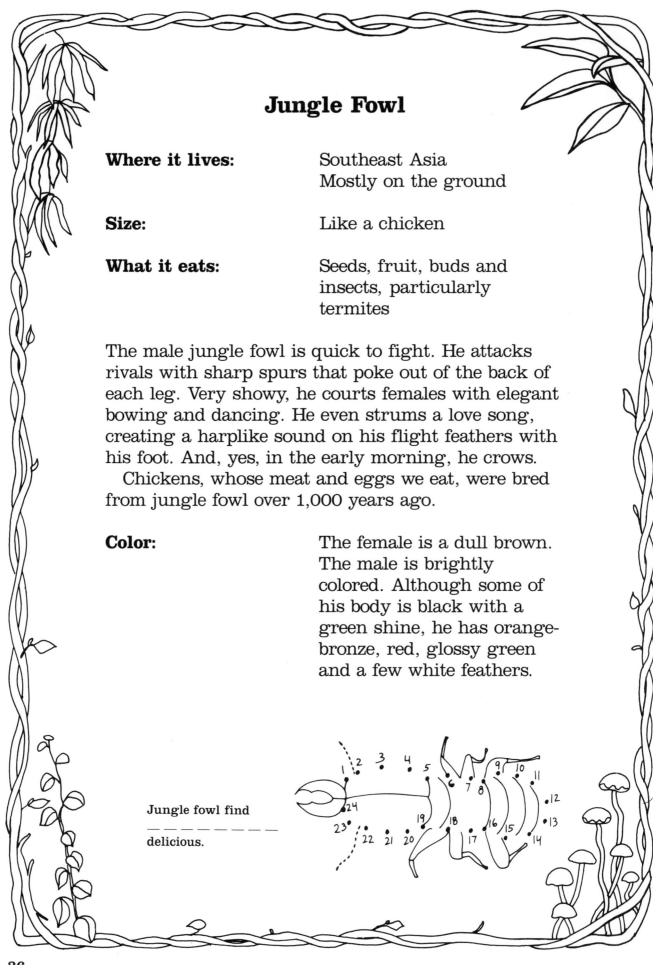

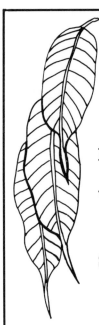

Katydid

Pronounced:	KAY-tee-did
Where it lives:	In all rainforests Among leaves
Size:	Leaf-size, generally one-half to about three inches (1—7.6cm)
What it eats:	Leaves

The katydid matches its environment so well, it is hard to see it at all. This insect has wings the shape of a leaf and markings that look like leaf veins. It is holding its antennae together so they look like the stick that connects the leaf to the tree. Its legs look like twigs. When disturbed, the katydid may hop away, but then it holds still or sways gently if there is any breeze, so that it blends in and is not seen.

Color:	Mostly greens and browns

Yummy _ _ _ _ _
for a katydid.

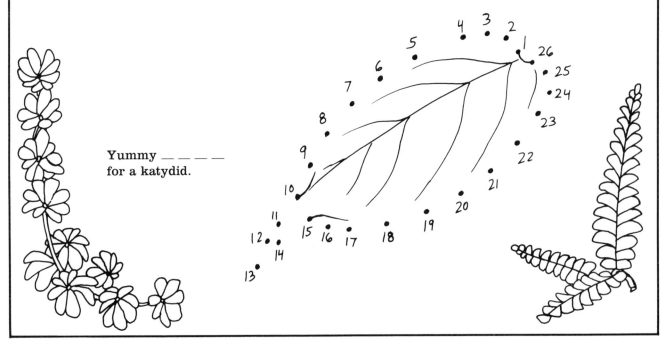

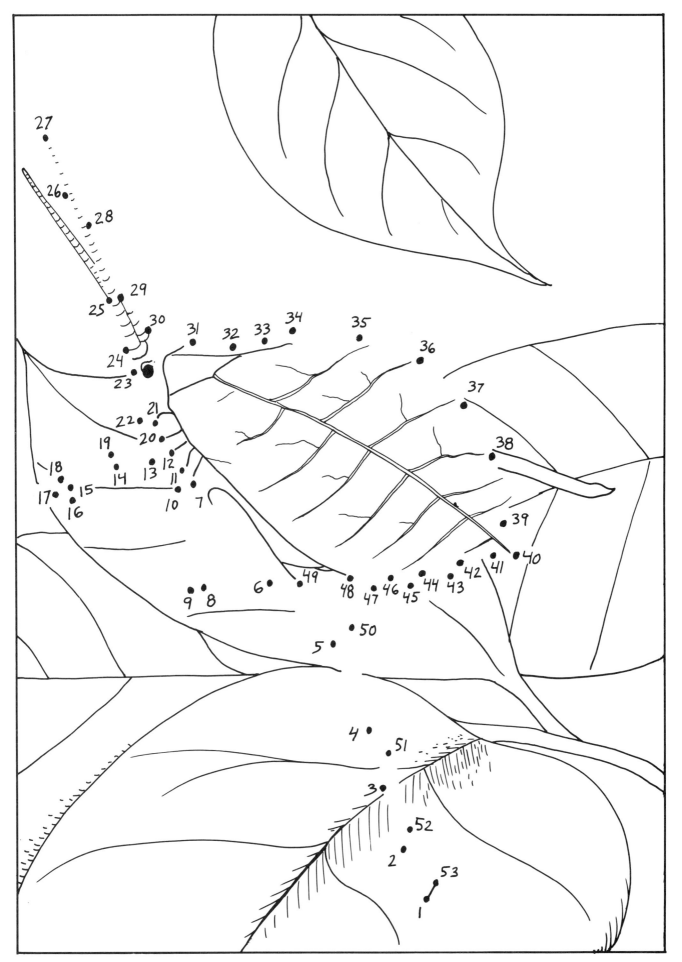

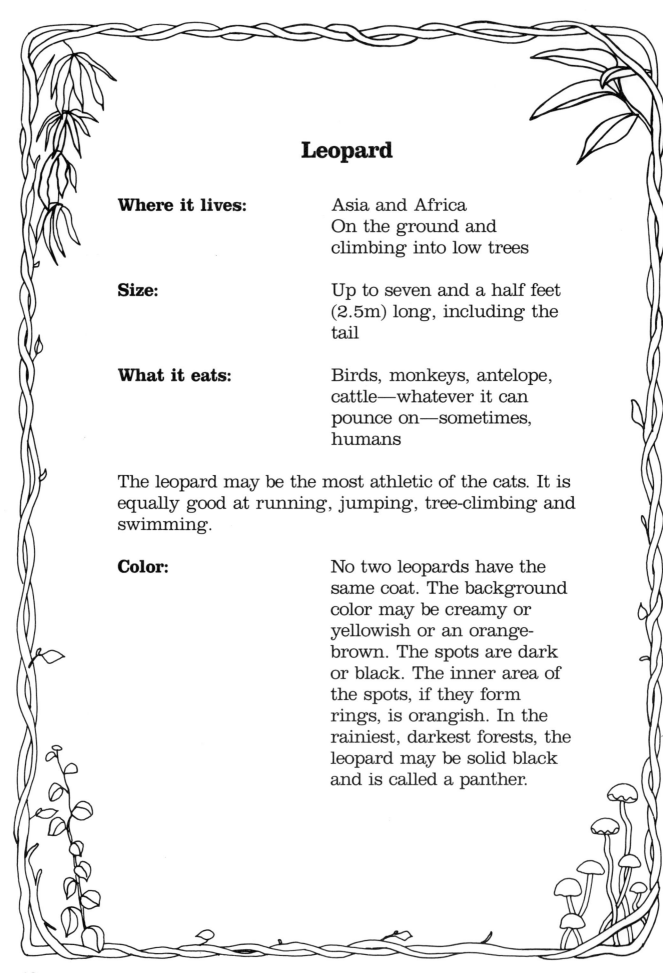

Leopard

Where it lives: Asia and Africa
On the ground and
climbing into low trees

Size: Up to seven and a half feet
(2.5m) long, including the
tail

What it eats: Birds, monkeys, antelope,
cattle—whatever it can
pounce on—sometimes,
humans

The leopard may be the most athletic of the cats. It is
equally good at running, jumping, tree-climbing and
swimming.

Color: No two leopards have the
same coat. The background
color may be creamy or
yellowish or an orange-
brown. The spots are dark
or black. The inner area of
the spots, if they form
rings, is orangish. In the
rainiest, darkest forests, the
leopard may be solid black
and is called a panther.

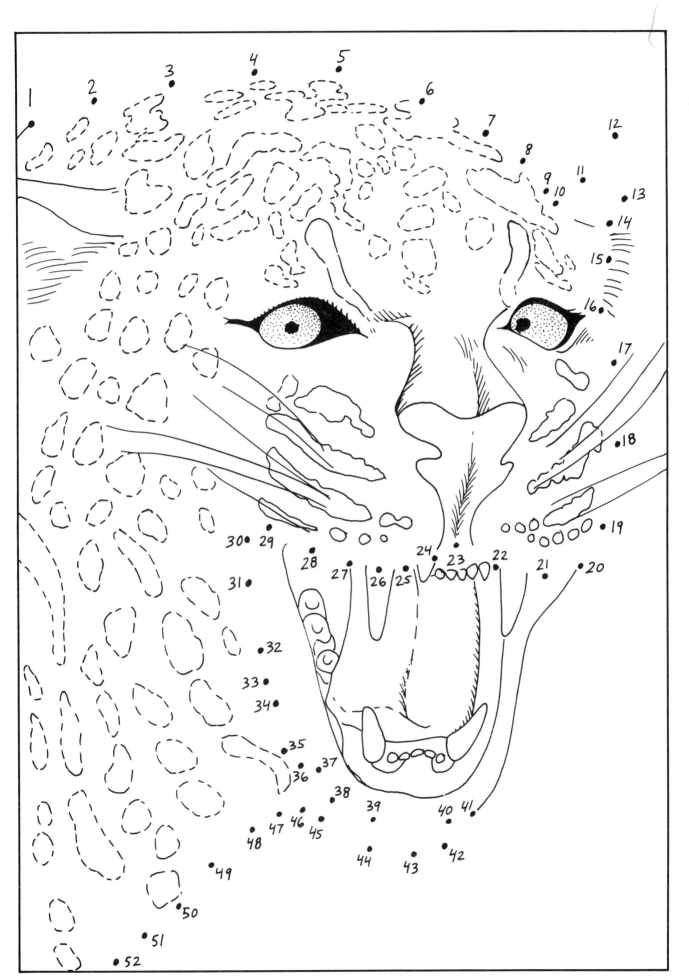

41

Macaw

Pronounced: muh-KAW

Where it lives: South America
In the trees, or sometimes
on a muddy cliff

Size: Macaws are the largest
parrots in the world—about
three feet (1m) long.

What it eats: Seed and fruit

The macaw, like all parrots, has great feet for
holding on to things. Two toes face forward and two
toes face back. Clamping onto a branch with one
foot, it uses the second foot to hold food. With its
strong, hooked beak, it can open hard-shelled nuts
as easily as you might bite an apple. It also uses its
beak as an extra foot when climbing.

Color: The macaw's feathers are
brightly colored in shades of
red, blue, green and yellow.

Brazil _ _ _ _
are very hard, but
macaws open them
easily.

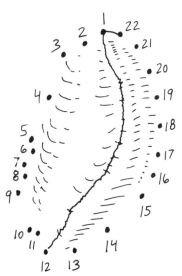

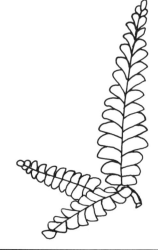

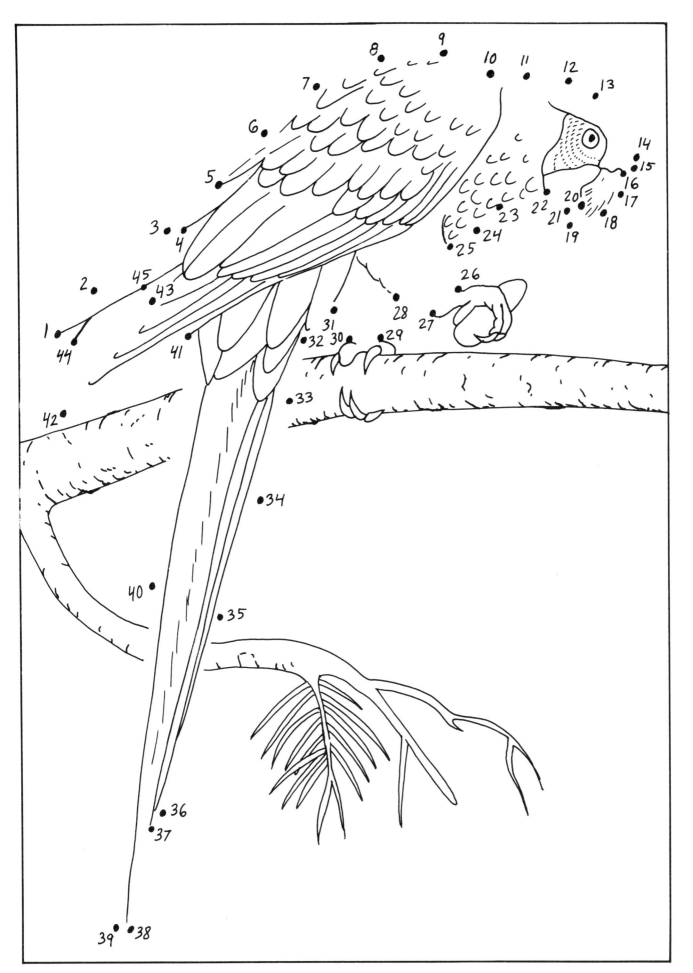

Mosquito

Where it lives: In all rainforests
Some kinds stay in the tree
canopy; some remain near
the ground; and others
move up and down.

Size: Generally, a quarter to half
an inch (.6—1.2cm) long

What it eats: Male mosquitos sip nectar
and female mosquitos suck
blood from people and
animals. The females do
this to get protein for
manufacturing eggs.

Mosquito bites itch because the soon-to-be-a-mother
mosquito squirts a little saliva under the skin as she
sucks your blood. The saliva keeps the blood from
clotting—and it irritates your skin. In the rainforest,
that saliva also can carry viruses that produce the
diseases called malaria and yellow fever.

Color: Grey

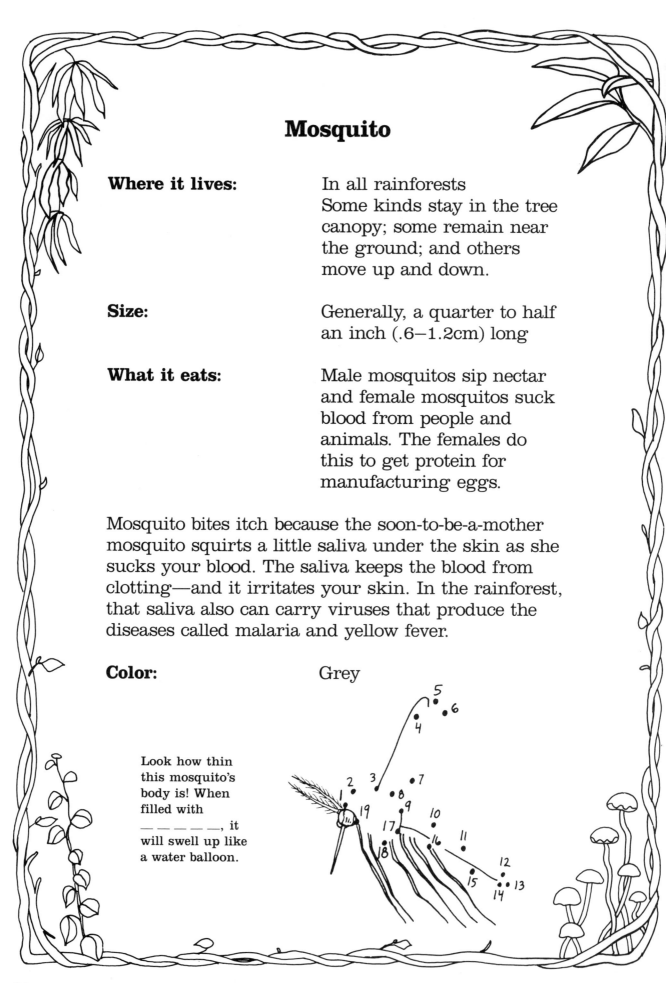

Look how thin
this mosquito's
body is! When
filled with
_ _ _ _ _, it
will swell up like
a water balloon.

44

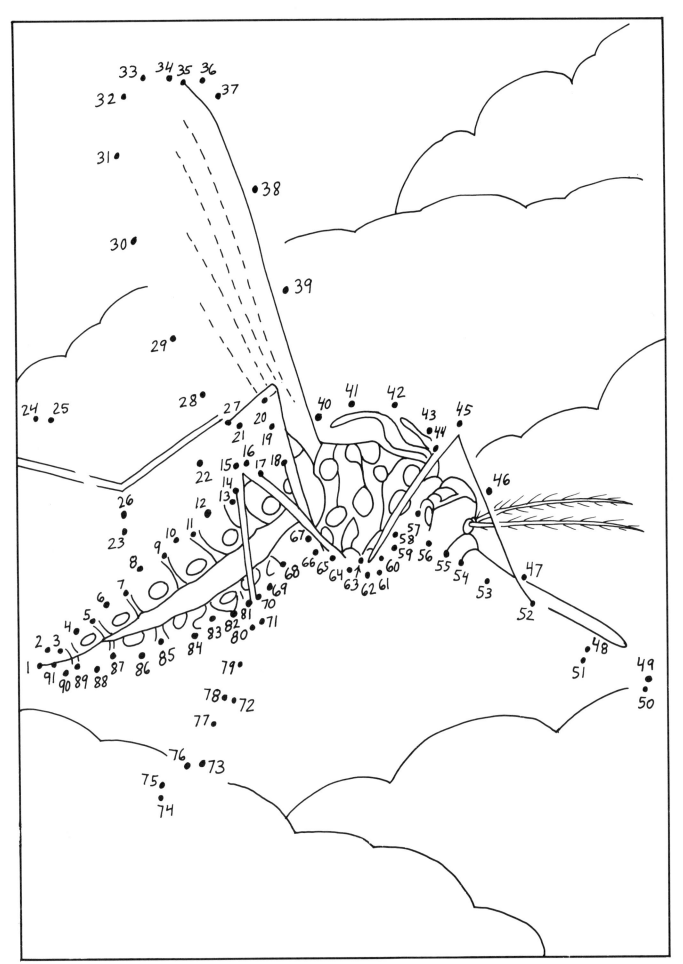

Okapi

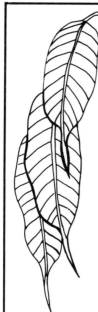

Pronounced:	oh-KAH-pee
Where it lives:	Africa On the ground
Size:	About the size of a horse—over six feet (1.8m) long from head to rump, and five and a half feet (1.7m) high at the shoulder
What it eats:	Leaves. Unlike the horse, the okapi does not graze from the grass on the ground, but reaches for leaves as high and low as its neck can stretch. With a long, rough tongue, it strips leaves from trees and bushes.

Pygmies have hunted it for centuries, but European explorers didn't even know of the okapi's existence until 1901. When they first saw it, explorers assumed it was a kind of zebra because of its size and stripes. Actually, the okapi is more like a giraffe. Many of its body parts and behaviors are like the giraffe's. For instance, both have back legs shorter than front legs, and both stretch their necks to eat leaves. The okapi's tongue is so long it also uses it to clean its eyes and eyelashes.

Color:	Brownish black with white stripes

Orangutan

Pronounced: uh-RANG-uh-tan

Where it lives: Southeast Asia
Mostly in the trees

Size: Males are five feet (1.5m)
tall and 220 pounds
(100kg)—like short, heavy
football players. Their
armspan may reach eight
feet (2.4m). Females are half
the size of males.

What it eats: Leaf buds and fruit

In the Malay language, orangutan means "jungle
man."

Due to forest destruction, fewer than 5,000
orangutans remain in the wild. In captivity, adult
males can become bad-tempered, even dangerous.

Color: Orange-brown

Orangutans eat litchi nuts,
which are really a

— — — — — .

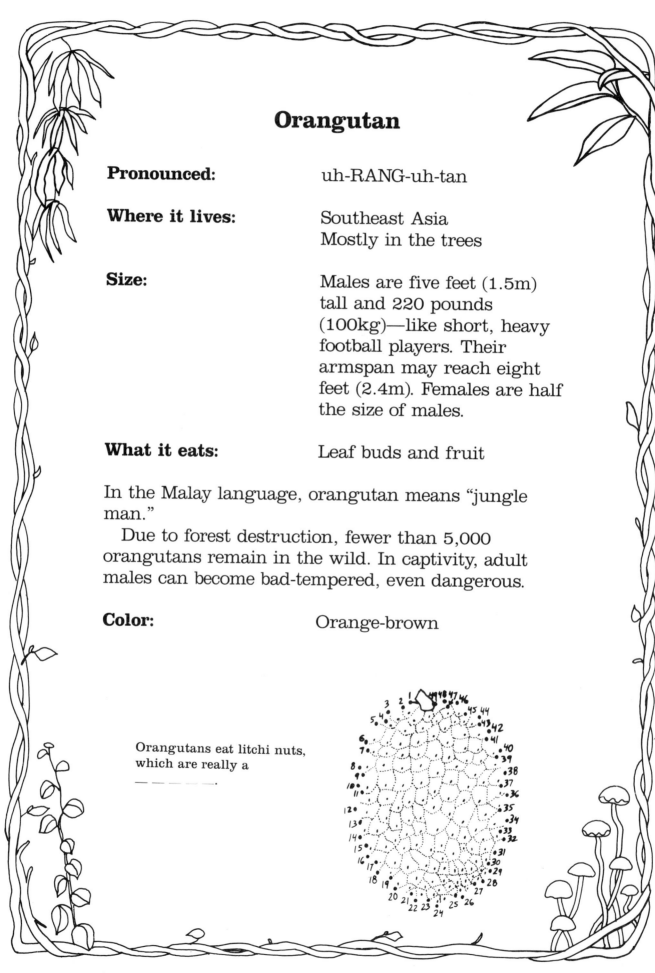

49

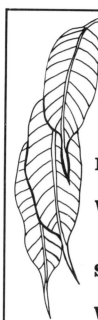

Red Piranha

Pronounced:	red puh-RAH-na
Where it lives:	South America In rivers and lakes
Size:	Up to 14 inches (35cm) long
What it eats:	Meat

The red piranha is one of the most ferocious fish in the world. Each fish can bite off only a thimbleful of flesh at a time, but because they swim in schools of hundreds, they can devour something the size of a cow in just a few minutes! They have eaten people, too.

Take a look at the piranha's teeth. They are shaped like triangles. The teeth in the bottom row have wiggly edges like those on steak knives. South American natives use piranha jaws for cutting hair, wood—just about anything.

Color:	Blue on upper body and tail, golden brown on belly and lower fins, green upper fin, grey lower lip, reddish brown eyes

Sloth

Pronounced: slawth

Where it lives: Central and South America In the tree canopy

Size: About 2 feet (.6m) long and 9 to 16 pounds (4 to 7kg)— about as big as a human baby

What it eats: Tree leaves

On the ground, the sloth is like a fish out of water. It cannot stand, cannot walk and is completely defenseless. Its body is made for hanging upside down. From that position it can feed, sleep, breed, walk, whistle and shed rain.

Most of the time, the sloth hangs very still. When it moves, it moves so-o-o-o slowly. For example, a mother sloth was seen "hurrying" to her baby at 15 feet (4.5m) per hour. Imagine taking an hour to cross your room!

Color: The fur is a greyish brown. Blue-green algae grow in grooves in the fur. During the wettest seasons, the algae bloom and the sloth looks darker and greenish— a natural punk hairdo!

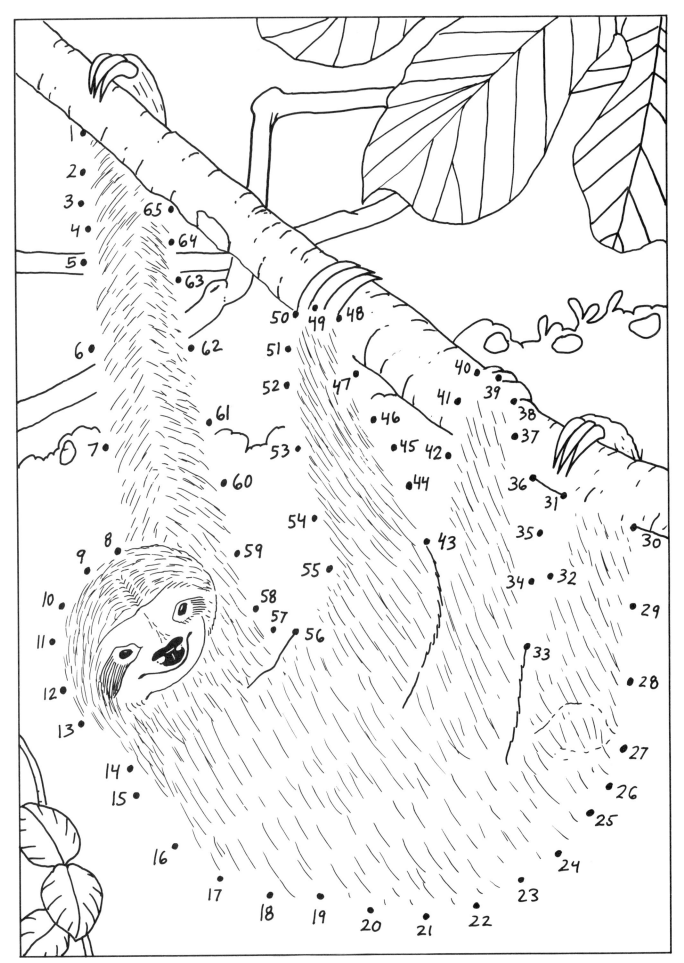

53

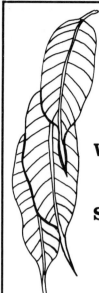

Spider Monkey

Where it lives: Central and South America
                             In the trees

Size: A foot and a half (.5m) long
                             from head to toe, if
                             stretched really straight,
                             and weighing 10 pounds
                             (4.5kg)

What it eats: Leaves, fruit, nuts, insects
                             and other small animals

The spider monkey is the acrobat of the forest. It moves quickly, swinging from branch to branch, hanging by its tail or by its legs. It leaps from one tree to another, sometimes as far as 35 feet (10.6m).

The spider monkey uses its tail as we do our hands. With its tail, it can pluck fruit, flowers and budding leaves at the end of branches that other animals can't reach. Spider monkeys "hold tails" instead of holding hands, especially mothers and children.

Color: Some spider monkeys are
                             pretty much all black; some
                             are reddish brown; others
                             are a mix of black and
                             brown.

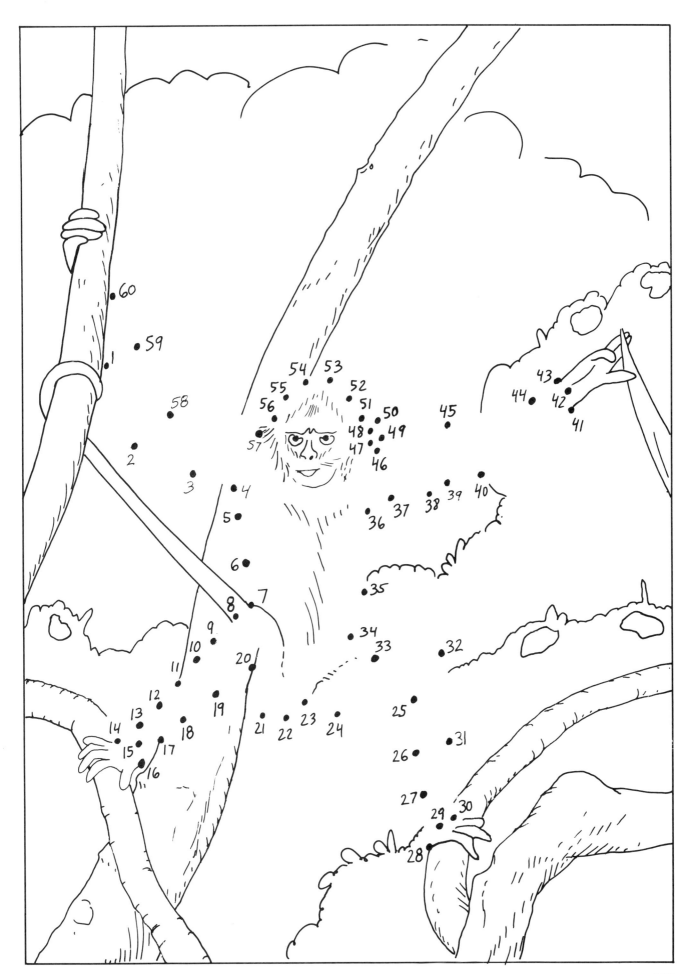

Tamandua

Pronounced:	TAH-man-DWA
Where it lives:	South America In the trees
Size:	About as large as a fox
What it eats:	Ants and especially termites

The tamandua is a kind of anteater. It eats ants *and* termites. It climbs in the trees, using its tail to help hold it steady as it raids termite nests. Its powerful arms and sharp claws rip open the nests easily. Its strength is amazing: there are stories of tamanduas killing jaguars and even humans who pester them.

Color:	Greyish cream and black

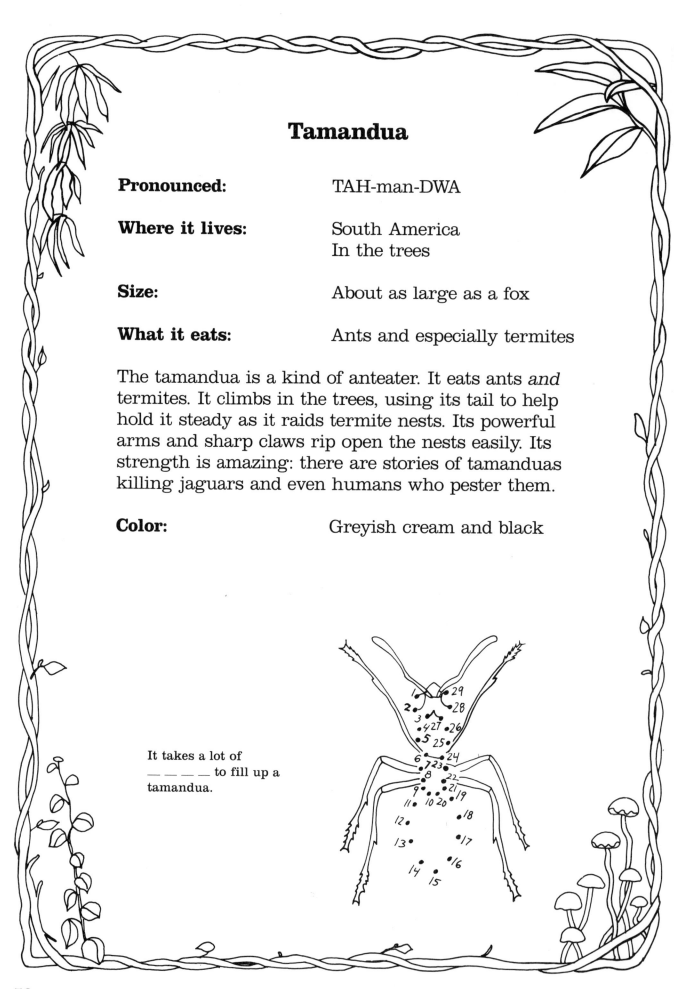

It takes a lot of
_ _ _ _ to fill up a
tamandua.

Tarantula

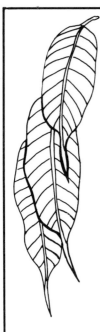

Pronounced: tuh-RAN-choo-luh

Where it lives: In all rainforests. The giant tarantula at the right, however, lives only in South America.
On the ground

Size: The giant tarantula is as big as a dinner plate! Its body alone is 3½ inches (9cm) long. When it extends its legs, it is 10 inches (25cm) in diameter. It's the largest living spider in the world. Other tarantulas are much smaller.

What it eats: Insects, small rodents, reptiles and birds

The tarantula waits out the day in its burrow or under a rock or some bark. At night it goes looking for food. It pounces on its prey and injects poison from two fangs that look like extra legs. The poison paralyzes the prey and starts digesting it. Then the spider sucks up the contents of the animal's body, as you would a milkshake.

Color: Brown

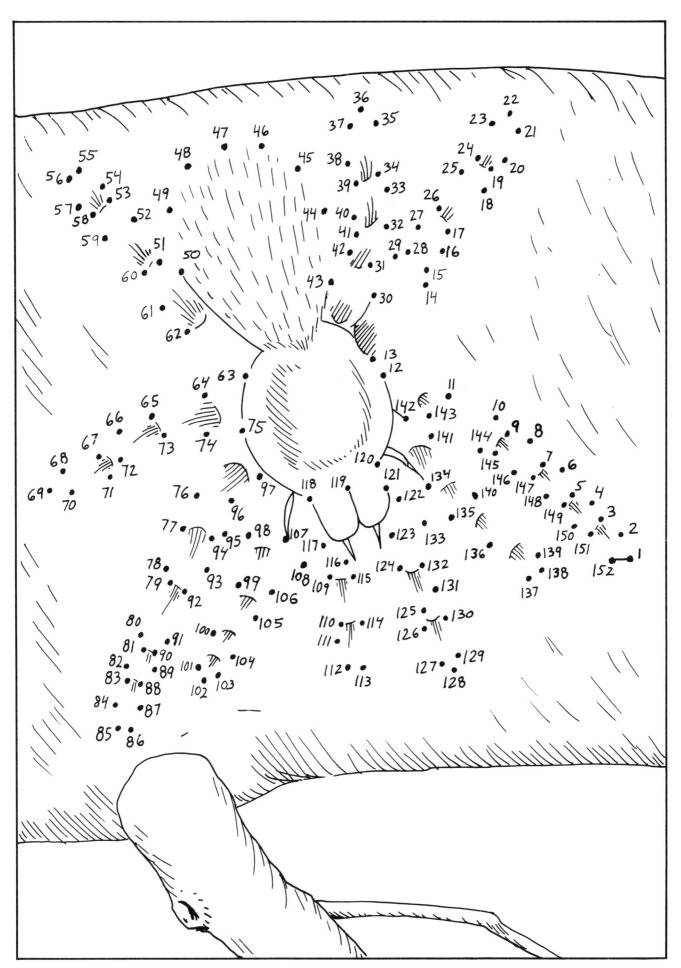

Tiger

Where it lives: Asia
Mostly on the ground

Size: Including the tail, it may
grow to 9½ feet (2.9m)
long—as long as some cars.

What it eats: Deer, pigs, monkeys, dogs,
rats, snakes, lizards, birds
and fish

The tiger is the largest cat in the jungle. However,
very few are left, because there is not much jungle
left for them to live in and find food.

    The tiger doesn't like the heat. It spends hot days
lying in pools and streams. It roars to call its mate or
cubs and to defend its area. Its roar can be heard a
mile away.

Color: Black stripes, a creamy
belly and inner legs, and an
orangish brown back and
sides

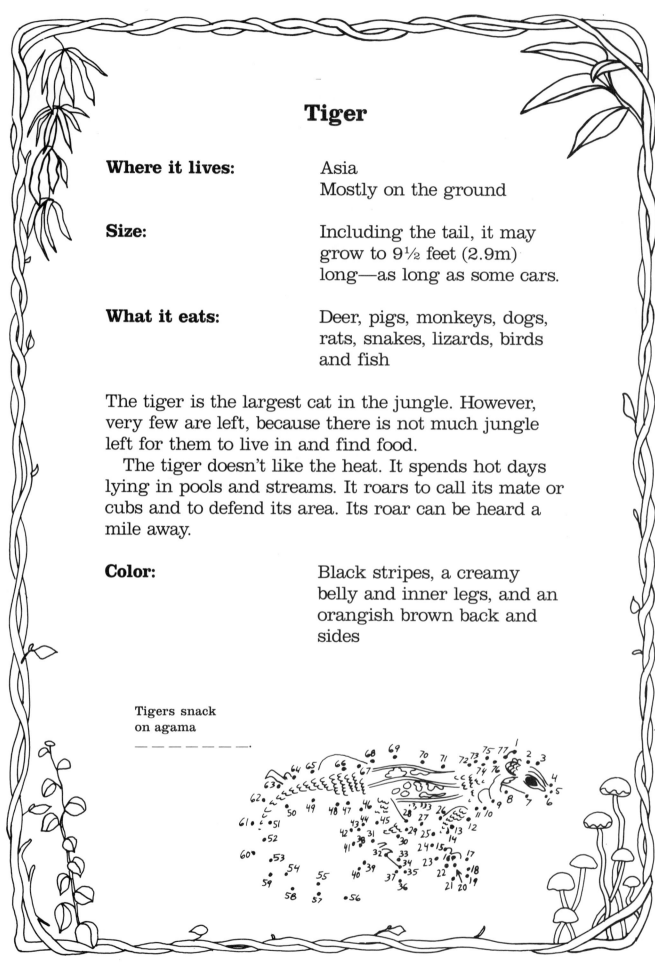

Tigers snack
on agama

Toucan

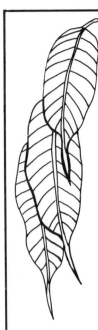

Pronounced: TOO-kan

Where it lives: South America
In the trees

Size: One to two feet (.3—.6m)
long. The beak in some
toucans is over half the
length of the bird!

What it eats: Mostly fruit, but every now
and then a frog or a bug or
some bird's eggs.

Toucans are a friendly, noisy bunch. They make
short glides about the trees, gathering fruit and
chattering in groups of about a dozen. Their nests
are in holes high up in the trees.

Color: Basically black with a white
throat and splashy colors on
the beak. The bright colors
include shades of red,
orange, yellow, green, blue,
purple and white.

Toucans pluck palm
fruit and toss it in
their _ _ _ _ _ _ _
as we sometimes do
with popcorn.

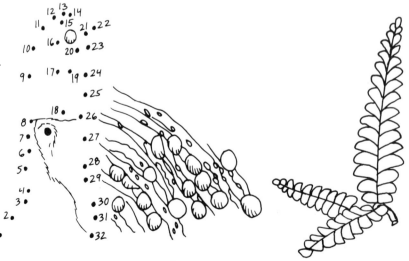

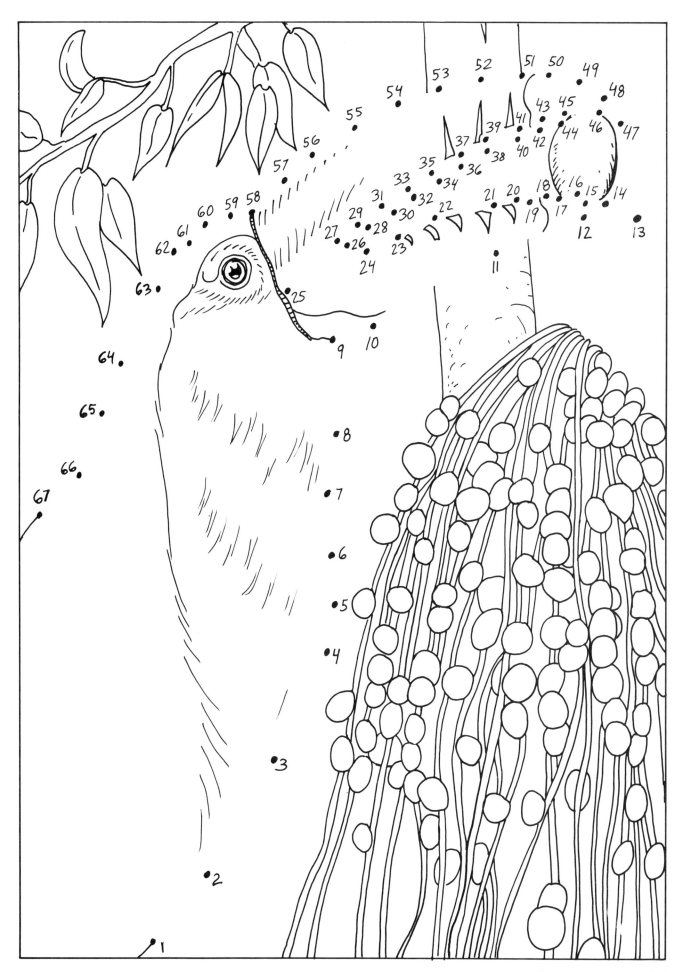

Index

ANSWERS   6-pigs; 10-insect; 12-flowers; 14-flies; 16-bananas; 18-opossum; 20-flying squirrel; 22-gibbons; 24-leaves; 26-monkey; 28-rotting; 30-fig; 32-nectar; 36-termites; 38-leaf; 42-nuts; 44-blood; 48-fruit; 56-ants; 60-lizards; 62-mouths.